Pocket Guide to
BALSAM
BASHING

and how to tackle other
INVASIVE NON-NATIVE SPECIES
Theo Pike

First published in Great Britain by Merlin Unwin Books, 2014
Copyright © Theo Pike

Merlin Unwin Books Ltd
Palmers House, 7 Corve Street, Ludlow, Shropshire SY8 1DB
www.merlinunwin.co.uk

The author asserts his moral right to be identified with this work.
Designed and set in Helvetica Neue by Merlin Unwin
Printed by Leo Paper Products

ISBN 978 1 906122 62 1

In memory of Peter Lapsley
Flyfisher, conservationist, writer and friend

The author has made every effort to ensure that the information in
this book is correct at the time of going to press. However, legal
regulations and other details may be subject to change: if in doubt,
please check with your local environmental regulator *(see page 4)*.

Because they can damage our environment so severely, INNS are
covered by a complicated range of laws which may soon be joined by
EU regulations. At the same time, some INNS are protected except
when they're harming native species, crops or public health.

You can find summaries of the latest legal situation on the
GB Non Native Species Secretariat (GBNNSS) website at:
www.nonnativespecies.org, and on the Invasive Species Ireland
website at: **www.invasivespeciesireland.com**

CONTENTS

USEFUL LINKS & LEGAL STUFF

If you're in any doubt about the legal status of any invasive non-native species (INNS) you'd like to control, you should consult one or more of the following for the latest guidelines and legal information:

Natural England: www.naturalengland.org.uk
Environment Agency, England: www.environment-agency.gov.uk
Scottish Natural Heritage: www.snh.gov.uk
Scottish Environment Protection Agency: www.sepa.org.uk
Natural Resources Wales: www.naturalresourceswales.gov.uk
Department of the Environment, Northern Ireland: www.doeni.gov.uk
Environmental Protection Agency, Ireland: www.epa.ie
Inland Fisheries Ireland: www.fisheriesireland.ie
European Commission: www.ec.europa.eu/environment/nature/invasivealien

You can also get detailed specialist and legal advice from:
GBNNSS: www.nonnativespecies.org
Invasive Species Ireland: www.invasivespeciesireland.com
Invasive Species in Northern Ireland: www.habitas.org.uk/invasive
Food & Environment Research Agency (FERA): www.fera.defra.gov.uk
Invasive Non-Native Specialists' Association: www.innsa.org
Your local Rivers Trust: www.theriverstrust.org and www.rafts.org.uk
Your local Wildlife Trust: www.wildlifetrusts.org
Angling Trust: www.anglingtrust.net
British Association for Shooting and Conservation: www.basc.org.uk
CAB International: www.cabi.org
Freshwater Habitats Trust: www.freshwaterhabitats.org.uk
Game & Wildlife Conservation Trust: www.gwct.org.uk
Plantlife: www.plantlife.org.uk
Royal Horticultural Society: www.rhs.org.uk
The Conservation Volunteers: www.tcv.org.uk
The Green Blue: www.thegreenblue.org.uk
Woodland Trust: www.woodlandtrust.org.uk

Last but not least, you can help everyone by reporting your sightings of INNS as soon as possible:

See website addresses on page 9.

WHAT ARE INVASIVE NON-NATIVE SPECIES?

Within the last few years we've all become much more familiar with the idea of invasive species. Plants and animals as varied as giant hogweed, zebra mussels and oak processionary moths regularly make headlines because of the health, environmental and economic problems they cause. Invasive deer contribute to more than 74,000 traffic accidents in the UK every year, while Japanese knotweed added £70m to the bill for staging the London Olympics, and could even stop you getting a mortgage on your house.

So what exactly are **invasive non-native species (INNS)**? And what can you and I do about them?

Scientists usually define INNS as plants or animals which cause unacceptable damage after being spread by humans, by mistake or on purpose, beyond the areas where they naturally evolved.

In their new homes, which they've often reached by means of international trade, transport, travel or tourism, INNS thrive where the environment is already unbalanced by urban development and other human activities. Free from their natural enemies, competitors and parasites, they multiply and spread rapidly along roads, railway lines, footpaths and rivers, out-competing native species and altering whole landscapes and ecosystems. They destroy crops and forestry, dump silt into rivers, sabotage flood defences, drains and electrical infrastructure, cut off access to beautiful places, and drive rare and iconic species into extinction. And they cost us all a lot of money - at least £1.8bn to the UK economy, €203m to Ireland, and more than €12bn of damage across the whole of Europe every year.

Not all introduced species turn invasive – in fact, most of the world's food supplies probably derive from species which didn't originate where they're now grown. But those that do make their escape, and spread unchecked into new areas, are shifting us all towards a state of homogeneity that's been dubbed global blandification: a world where, as David Quammen wrote in 1998, virtually everything will live virtually everywhere, but the list of species that constitute 'everything' will be very small.

As a result, INNS are right up there with climate change and habitat destruction as a global threat to biodiversity and even our own way of life. Many experts now believe that we live in the Anthropocene age – a time when human impacts on our planet have altered its natural equilibrium so radically that we need to manage what's left to restore any kind of balance, and ensure we still have the resources and life-support systems we need for our own existence. True, our environment may no longer be totally pristine, but that's no reason not to try to preserve what we've still got, and restore some of what we've lost. And if any particular species does escape from its native range to start wreaking havoc

The River Monnow: choked by a jungle of Himalayan balsam…

Before

on the landscapes, ecosystems and natural processes we all love and depend on, it's in all our interests to do something about it.

Across Britain and Ireland, native plants and animals are classified as those which colonised these islands naturally at the end of the last Ice Age, 10,000 years ago, before rising sea levels submerged the land bridges between them and mainland Europe. Using their wings, flying birds and insects from our common northern European bioregion have continued to colonise naturally since then. But these and many of our other native species are now under threat from around 2,000 INNS which have arrived from more distant parts of the world and established themselves successfully. More than 600 have arrived since 1950 alone, many have turned aggressively invasive, and increasing numbers are on their way.

How can you help stop this expensive, dangerous (and ultimately very boring) slide towards global blandification?

Read on and find out more!

...and after clearance by the Monnow Rivers Association's volunteers.

HOW TO USE THIS BOOK

Recent research reveals strong scientific evidence that global biodiversity actually hinges on local action. So there's never been a better time to protect the natural character of the world on your doorstep.

All the invasive non-native species (INNS) in this guide have been carefully selected, with expert advice from Defra, the Environment Agency (EA) and other professional bodies, because you're likely to encounter them somewhere in the British Isles. And because it's easy for you to do something about them.

From reporting sightings with an app on your mobile, to pulling Himalayan balsam as your summer 'green gym' session, you really can make a difference and help restore environmental balance on your local patch.

Here's how you can help:

✳ **Use this book to discover what INNS you can expect to find** in your area, and practice your identification skills to save confusion with lookalike species

✳ **Keep an eye on the Species Alerts page** on the GB Non Native Species Secretariat (GBNNSS) website and report any sightings of these species immediately (www.nonnativespecies.org/alerts)

✳ **Report any sightings** to RISC, Alien Watch or other recording schemes *(see opposite page)* as soon as possible: this will help to collect useful data on the spread and behaviour of these INNS

✳ **Find and join a local action group**, such as Rivers Trusts, Wildlife Trusts or conservation volunteers, all of which may be active in managing INNS (check out the projects database at www.nonnativespecies.org/maps) – or start a group of your own!

✳ **Take direct action by hand pulling, cutting, trapping** etc as appropriate (always using the latest best practice, with the landowner's permission, and ideally as part of a wider co-ordinated eradication project)

✳ **Take careful biosecurity measures** when you're travelling, especially around water *(see pages 88-89)*

✳ **Don't allow INNS to escape** into the wild (many are covered by strict legislation: *see page 4*)

✳ **Get trained and licensed** to use pesticides and herbicides: using herbicides near water usually requires approval from your local environmental regulator as well as technical competence qualifications (National Proficiency Test Council or equivalent)

✳ **Spread the word**: help other people understand the threat of INNS

REPORT YOUR SIGHTINGS

GB Non-Native Species Secretariat's Species Alert system
www.nonnativespecies.org/alerts

RISC (Recording Invasive Species Counts)
www.nonnativespecies.org/recording

Alien Watch (Ireland)
www.invasivespeciesireland.com/alien-watch

PlantTracker app
http://planttracker.naturelocator.org

Your local environmental records centre
www.alerc.org.uk

© GBNNSS

AMERICAN SKUNK CABBAGE
Lysichiton americanus

Where does it come from and how did it get here?

American skunk cabbage comes from the Pacific Northwest of America, where it's reputedly eaten by bears as a laxative after winter hibernation. The stem produces heat to melt through surrounding snow and disperse its scent in cold air. Brought to the UK in 1901 as an ornamental garden plant, skunk cabbage has escaped and naturalised in many marshy areas.

Skunk cabbage grows up to 1.5m in height, with leathery leaves and yellow hood-like flowers.

Widely sold by garden centres, this plant can also be identified by its pungent, skunky smell.

What's the problem?

American skunk cabbage is one of several species that is gradually being recognised as a threat to British biodiversity at a national level. It tolerates all types of soil, and can easily invade wet woodland, pond margins and streamsides, even out-competing other invasive species like Himalayan balsam.

By forming dense stands, it shades out native plants with its huge leathery leaves, which emerge early and last for much of the growing season. As a result, rare species-rich wetlands can be dramatically degraded. Skunk cabbage berries can spread long distances along waterways, and via birds and mammals.

What can I do about it?

If you find American skunk cabbage growing in the wild, and you get the landowner's permission, you can help to control it by:

* Spraying with glyphosate between June and October

* Reporting any sightings to the RISC or Alien Watch recording schemes, or the UK's PlantTracker app *(see page 9)*

Spraying skunk cabbage is easiest at times of low rainfall or drought, when access to boggy areas is firmer and safer. Controlling any plant by spraying herbicides near water almost always needs approval from your relevant environmental regulator *(see page 4)* as well as technical competence qualifications (National Proficiency Test Council or equivalent).

If you want to keep skunk cabbage as an ornamental plant in your garden, you can still help to stop it escaping by following the Be Plant Wise biosecurity guidelines *(see page 95)*. In particular, dispose of any cuttings carefully, and try to stop the berries dispersing beyond your own property.

© GBNNSS / (inset) Snowdonia National Parks Authority

HIMALAYAN BALSAM
Impatiens glandulifera

Where does it come from and how did it get here?

Popularly known as bee bums, policeman's helmet and poor man's orchid, Himalayan balsam was introduced from Kashmir to Kew Gardens in 1839. Escapee colonies appeared in Hertfordshire and Middlesex by 1855, and the plant is now widespread across the UK and Ireland, forming dense monoculture stands along many rivers.

Main picture: Himalayan balsam's sweet-scented pink and white flowers appear between June and October.

Inset: Up to 800 spring-loaded floating seeds can be fired up to 7m from each parent plant.

Below: The invasive but less vigorous orange balsam (Impatiens capensis) reached the UK in 1822.

© Stacy Whalen

What's the problem?

Himalayan balsam is the tallest annual plant in Britain, growing up to 3m high. Studies suggest that it can reduce native plant diversity by up to two-thirds: first shading out native species, then out-competing them for the attention of bees and other pollinators with its long flowering time and plentiful nectar. Native insect numbers are also reduced.

When the shallow-rooted plants die back in autumn, river banks are left bare and vulnerable to erosion. Soil is then eroded by winter floods and dumped in river gravels as silt, suffocating insects and fish eggs.

What can I do about it?

Planting or otherwise causing Himalayan balsam to grow in the wild is against the law in the UK and Ireland. With the landowner's permission, you can help to control it by:

✳ Pulling it up before the seed pods start exploding, ideally before the plant can flower or set seed

✳ Cutting each plant below the lowest node of the stem (if you cut above this point, it can still re-sprout)

✳ Spraying with glyphosate (if near water, regulatory approval is likely to be required)

✳ Allowing sheep or cows to graze young plants

✳ Reporting any sightings to the RISC or Alien Watch recording schemes, or the UK's PlantTracker app *(see page 9)*

Compost or pile up the plants in a shady spot, where stems and leaves will wilt and dessicate quickly: few seeds will germinate in future years. On a river or stream, work downstream from the headwaters, so the area you've cleared isn't recolonised from upstream. Revisit monthly, then keep checking occasionally for at least 3 years to exhaust the seed bank: you can also help to restore native species by re-sowing with a suitable meadow seed mix.

For more information visit: **www.nonnativespecies.org**
and **www.invasivespeciesireland.com**

GIANT HOGWEED

Heracleum mantegazzianum

Don't touch!
It presents a serious public health risk. Each bristle carries a drop of phototoxic sap, which can cause recurring sunburn and even blindness.

Where does it come from and how did it get here?

Native to the Caucasus mountains of Russia, giant hogweed was prized by Victorian plant collectors for its 'Herculean proportions' and 'splendid invasiveness' when they brought it to Britain. These characteristics helped it to escape from estate parklands and spread widely, often along the banks of large rivers like the Wye, Usk, Tweed and Mulcair.

What's the problem?

As Europe's tallest herbaceous plant, giant hogweed grows to 5m high, forming dense colonies which shade out other plants. Each plant can self-fertilise, taking several years to fully mature before flowering only once in late spring or early summer, setting up to 50,000 seeds.

Brushing against its bristly leaves and red-blotched stems can transfer beads of sap to skin, resulting in blisters and third degree burns, recurring for years with every exposure to the sun. These burns may even require hospital treatment.

What can I do about it?

Planting or otherwise causing giant hogweed to grow in the wild is against the law in the UK and Ireland. With the landowner's permission, you can help to control it by:

* Cutting each plant's tap-root with a spade 15cm below ground level
* Cutting off and burning the flowering heads, after they've set seed but before seed has scattered: follow-up visits may be necessary
* Spraying the tops and undersides of leaves with glyphosate as early as possible, at least twice during the growing season (if near water, regulatory approval is likely to be required)
* Injecting each stem with glyphosate, using a special injection kit (contact your local council or INNS action group for training in herbicide use)
* Reporting any sightings to Ireland's Alien Watch recording scheme, or the UK's PlantTracker app *(see page 9)*

Always wear full protective clothing, including eye protection, and remember that giant hogweed's sap-tipped bristles can easily penetrate light fabric. In case of contact with the sap, wash any affected skin at once and shield it from sunlight for at least 48 hours.

 Giant hogweed should never be strimmed or composted: cuttings are legally classified as controlled waste.

© GENNSS

JAPANESE KNOTWEED

Fallopia japonica

Where does it come from and how did it get here?

As its name suggests, Japanese knotweed's native range is Japan (where ironically it's now rare) as well as North Korea and parts of China. Much admired for its architectural proportions and the lacy effect of its leaves and flowers, it was brought to the Netherlands in 1849. It was recorded growing wild in south Wales in 1886 and has become pervasive throughout the UK and Ireland.

Main picture: Japanese knotweed grows in dense thickets up to 3m high, which crowd out other plants before dying back below ground in the autumn. With brittle, fleshy, bamboo-like stems, knotweed can form a new plant from a fragment as small as a fingernail, spreading easily along watercourses and in garden waste. Inset and below: It can even grow through walls and tarmac!

© (insets) Japanese Knotweed Solutions

What's the problem?

Reputedly evolved to grow through hardened lava on Mount Fuji, Japanese knotweed now has a fearsome reputation for doing the same with concrete and tarmac, including flood defences, across the western world.

It flourishes in disturbed environments, spreading 7m a year via underground rhizomes whilst tolerating acid soil, heavy metal contamination and air pollution. Eradication from development sites is required by UK law, and it's often impossible to get a mortgage on property where knotweed is present. Clearing it from the London 2012 Olympics site cost £70 million, and Defra estimates that the total UK eradication bill would rise to more than £1.5 billion. Even more invasive variants could be produced by accidental hybridisation with giant knotweed or Russian vine.

What can I do about it?

Planting or otherwise causing Japanese knotweed to grow in the wild is against the law in the UK and Ireland. With the landowner's permission, you can help to control it by:

* Fencing off until winter, then cut and burn dead growth to let frost weaken the rhizomes, and spray with glyphosate over 3 years

* Injecting each stem with glyphosate, using a special injection kit, in late summer or early autumn, so the herbicide is drawn down into the rhizomes (contact your local council or INNS action group for training in herbicide use)

* Reporting sightings to your local council or the Alien Watch recording scheme, or the UK's PlantTracker app *(see page 9)*

Japanese knotweed should never be composted, and is classified as controlled waste. Even earth containing fragments of roots and stems must be disposed of at a licensed landfill site. Letting it spread from your property onto someone else's land is likely to be a private nuisance under civil law.

For more information visit: **www.nonnativespecies.org** *and* **www.invasivespeciesireland.com,** *or download the Japanese Knotweed Code of Practice at* **www.environment-agency.gov.uk**

© GBNNSS

PONTIC RHODODENDRON

Rhododendron ponticum

Where does it come from and how did it get here?

Pontic rhododendron was first recorded in the wild in Lincolnshire in 1894, having been introduced to Britain from Spain or Portugal in 1763. It was widely planted on Victorian estates for its ornamental value and as cover for game birds. Deliberate and accidental hybridisation with American species has produced a '*superponticum*' strain even better adapted to the British climate.

Pontic rhododendron can grow up to 8m in height, with purple flowers, woody stems and waxy leaves.

By taking over large areas of woodland, it's a major threat to endangered species like dormice, which need a mix of native trees, shrubs and plants to survive.

What's the problem?

Scientists think that Pontic rhododendron is one of the most damaging invasive species in semi-natural habitats in Britain, especially on acid soils in western and southern regions. Established rhododendrons form impenetrable jungles, outcompeting other plants for space and light: few native species survive, and natural cycles of woodland and moorland regeneration are interrupted.

Pontic rhododendron suppresses competition from surrounding plants by producing phenolic compounds in its leaves, which also make them unpalatable and even poisonous to grazing animals like sheep and deer. Wetlands and small streams can quickly be overshaded, with serious impacts on algae, insects and fish, and it's a major vector for the sudden oak death pathogen *(see page 88)*. Rhododendron honey may be poisonous to humans, causing intestinal and cardiac symptoms known as 'honey intoxication' or 'mad honey disease'.

What can I do about it?

Planting or otherwise causing Pontic rhododendron to grow in the wild is against the law in the UK and Ireland. With the landowner's permission, you can help to control it by:

* Cutting each plant manually or mechanically, followed by digging up and burning the roots

* Spraying any regrowth with glyphosate (if near water, regulatory approval is likely to be required)

* Reporting any sightings to the RISC or Alien Watch recording schemes, or the UK's PlantTracker app *(see page 9)*

Each rhododendron plant produces many million seeds, which are easily dispersed by wind into new areas, and can remain viable in the soil for several years. As a result, controlling invasive rhododendron is likely to require partnership on a landscape scale.

© Corey Raimond

© Alo Konsen

RAGWEED
Ambrosia artemisiifolia

Where does it come from and how did it get here?

The first report of North American ragweed growing wild in the UK dates from 1836, when it was noticed in a hop garden in Kent. Since then, scientists believe it's been repeatedly re-introduced to many areas as a contaminant in bird seed and horticultural soil. Although now widespread across Europe, it's not yet considered self-sustaining in the British Isles.

Main picture: Ragweed grows up to 1m high with a stout central stem, lateral side branches, and deeply divided leaves about 15cm long.

Don't touch! *Ragweed can cause contact dermatitis, as well as hay fever when it flowers (see inset photo) from August to October.*

What's the problem?

If climate change helped ragweed to become fully established in Britain, it could spell severe discomfort for millions of hay fever sufferers every year. Ragweed spreads rapidly along railway lines, roadside verges and other marginal land: each annual plant produces around a billion highly allergenic pollen grains each season, which have reputedly been found 2 miles up in the atmosphere and 400 miles out to sea. Seeds can survive at least 5 years in the soil.

In areas colonised by ragweed, it soon becomes the main allergy-causing species. Ragweed pollen is one of the most common causes of hay fever, asthma attacks and even contact dermatitis in the USA, while research in Hungary shows that up to 60% of people are allergic to it. As such, ragweed could significantly extend the hay fever season in the UK beyond the main grass flowering season, adding millions of pounds to the annual cost of treating hay fever symptoms.

What can I do about it?

If you find ragweed growing in the wild, and you get the landowner's permission, you can help to control it by:

* Cutting each plant manually or mechanically, within half an inch of the ground, to prevent several branching stems re-sprouting in place of the original one: follow-up visits may be necessary

* Spraying with glyphosate (if near water, regulatory approval is likely to be required)

* Reporting any sightings to Ireland's Alien Watch recording scheme, or the UK's PlantTracker app *(see page 9)*

When handling ragweed, wear protective gloves and other clothing to avoid the possibility of dermatitis or hay fever symptoms being triggered by skin contact.

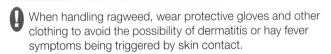

For more information visit: **www.nonnativespecies.org**
www.invasivespeciesireland.com
and **www.internationalragweedsociety.org**

© GBNNSS

SPANISH BLUEBELL
Hyacinthoides hispanica

Where does it come from and how did it get here?

Spanish bluebells were introduced to British gardens from the Iberian peninsula by 1683, finding favour with gardeners for their vigour and ability to grow almost anywhere. They were first recorded in the wild in 1909: the earliest report of hybrid bluebells (Spanish/British crosses) dates from 1963.

Above: Spanish bluebells have broad leaves, robust stalks, blue pollen and paler flowers, and smell less strongly and sweetly than native British bluebells.

Not to be confused with the native British bluebell, *Hyacinthoides non-scripta.*
Below: British bluebells are more narrowly tubular, a darker blue, and the flower head droops downwards. Look at the colour of the pollen: if it is creamy white then the bluebell is native.

© Michael Maggs

What's the problem?

According to Plantlife's Bluebells for Britain survey in 2003, the UK hosts almost half the world's population of the ancient woodland bluebell, *Hyacinthoides non-scripta*, which has been repeatedly voted Britain's favourite spring flower.

In many areas these true native bluebells are thought to be threatened by cross-breeding with Spanish bluebells, which produces a fully fertile hybrid, *Hyacinthoides x massartiana*. With a mixture of features from both parents, these are now very common in gardens, as well as churchyards, parks, lay-by areas, and other places where garden waste is dumped. Plantlife's survey found that around 1 in 6 bluebells in the UK's broadleaved woodlands is already a hybrid.

What can I do about it?

If you find Spanish bluebells growing in the wild, and you get the landowner's permission, you can help to control them by:

* Digging up the bulbs (but remember that all wild-growing <u>native</u> bluebells are protected by law)

To remove Spanish or hybrid bluebells, dig them up when they've finished flowering, keeping their leaves intact. Leave them to dry in the sun for up to a month to kill the bulbs, which should only be composted when they're thoroughly dry and dead, to avoid accidental propagation.

If you want to keep Spanish bluebells as an ornamental plant in your garden, you can still help to stop them escaping by following the Be Plant Wise biosecurity guidelines *(see page 95)*. In particular, dispose of any cuttings carefully, and try to stop the plants spreading beyond your own property.

© The Rowley Gallery

TREE-OF-HEAVEN

Ailanthus altissima

Main picture: Tree-of-heaven (here at Hilgrove Road, London) grows rapidly to 25m or more, with pinnate leaves like ash or walnut, and lots of suckers from the base of the trunk (see bottom right). Broken twigs and crushed leaves have an unpleasant smell like rancid cashew nuts.

Where does it come from and how did it get here?

Native to China and north Vietnam, tree-of-heaven was introduced to Europe in the 18th century for furniture-making (which proved unsuccessful) and was widely planted in streets and parks. In Britain it has spread along railway lines and other transport corridors, and is especially invasive in the London area.

© blog.rowleygallery.co.uk

What's the problem?

Tree-of-heaven is globally recognised as an invasive species, thriving in polluted and disturbed urban and rural habitats. It grows in thickets with powerful suckering roots which are capable of causing extensive damage to infrastructure like sewer pipes, pavements, building foundations and archaeological remains.

Spreading by means of winged seeds and clonal suckers extending up to 15m from the main plant, tree-of-heaven has often gone unnoticed in Britain, but this may soon alter as a result of climate change. Its economic impacts are already notorious in warmer climates in southern Europe and the USA, where it's known as the 'ghetto palm' or 'tree-of-hell'. It is highly drought-resistant and suppresses other plants by releasing allelopathic toxins: contact with its mildly toxic sap can cause dermatitis.

What can I do about it?

If you find tree-of-heaven growing in the wild, and you get the landowner's permission, you can help to control it by:

* Girdling (ring-barking) the main stem, and cutting it the following year

* Reporting any sightings to the RISC or Alien Watch recording schemes *(see page 9)*

Simply cutting tree-of-heaven tends to encourage even more vigorous growth, so pre-girdling individual trees is recommended as the best way to reduce their vitality and stop later suckers emerging from root fragments and stumps.

Seeds do not normally survive for more than a year.

❶ Wear protective gloves to pull young seedlings by hand, or spray with glyphosate: follow-up visits will almost certainly be required.

© GBNNSS

ASIAN HORNET
Vespa velutina

Where does it come from and how do we stop it invading?

Asian hornets haven't yet reached the British Isles, but are spreading rapidly across France after arriving in Bordeaux sometime before 2005. Native to China and northern India, where the climate is similar to southern Europe, they probably arrived via a container of pottery. They have also now been recorded in Spain, Portugal, Italy and Belgium.

Asian hornets are slightly smaller than the native British species, with a dark velvety thorax, black head and yellow-orange face.

Invasion by Asian hornets would put even more pressure on the British bee population, which has already been seriously damaged by the invasive varroa mite since 1992 (see page 88).

What's the problem?

If they spread to Britain, Asian hornets would present a serious threat to endangered native bees and other important pollinators as well as amateur and commercial honey production. They also pose a threat to human health and caused 6 deaths in France in 2009.

In their native range, Asian hornets are widely-known as major predators of honey bees, reputedly killing up to a third of some colonies by snatching guard bees as well as foragers returning to the beehive with nectar or pollen.

Asian hornets target individual bees by hovering over the entrance to the hive, charging them from below, forcing them to the ground, and paralysing them before carrying them back to their own colonies to feed their brood. Especially in autumn, hornets also make strenuous efforts to break into bee colonies to rob the brood and stores. They create nests in trees.

What can I do about it?

If you see Asian hornets, or find any sign of an infestation, you can help to control them by:

* In the UK, emailing details and a photograph to: **alert_nonnative@ceh.ac.uk**

* Reporting any sightings to the RISC or Alien Watch recording schemes *(see page 9)*

* Catching a hornet in a glass jar and sending it to FERA's National Bee Unit for examination (*see* **www.nationalbeeunit.co.uk**)

Asian hornets are not believed to be noticeably more aggressive towards humans than the UK's native hornets: however, for your own health and safely, do not disturb or provoke an active hornets' nest.

It is the UK government's plan to take all measures necessary to halt any invasion of the Asian hornet.

ASIAN TIGER MOSQUITO
Aedes albopictus

Where does it come from and how do we stop it invading?

Asian tiger mosquitoes haven't yet reached the British Isles, but are now prevalent in several southern European countries, especially Italy. First noted in Albania in 1979, they probably reached Europe from south east Asia via the intercontinental trade in used tyres, and have also appeared in the Netherlands with imported 'lucky bamboo'.

Adult Asian tiger mosquitoes are small and black, with distinctive white markings on their legs and abdomen.

A fatal outbreak of chikungunya fever in Italy in 2007 was linked to Asian tiger mosquitoes, as well as cases of chikungunya and dengue reported from France in 2010.

What's the problem?

If they spread to Britain and Ireland, Asian tiger mosquitoes could be a serious danger to people's health, since they've been linked to the spread of more than 20 tropical diseases including yellow and chikungunya fevers. They may also be able to act as a 'bridge vector', transmitting other pathogens like West Nile and LaCrosse viruses from animals to humans.

Eradication of small colonies has been possible in France and Belgium, but tiger mosquitoes have successfully established themselves in Italy, Israel and the USA, where they're now considered ineradicable despite millions of euros being spent on control.

Breeding in sheltered pools of water in gutters, water butts, cemetery vases and stored or discarded tyres, they outcompete resident species of mosquitoes, and could probably survive British winters in greenhouses or in the egg stage of their lifecycle (when they can also endure severe drying and even freezing).

Climate modelling by the University of Liverpool in 2012 suggested that warmer, wetter parts of the UK could become hotspots of Asian tiger mosquito activity between 2030 and 2050.

What can I do about it?

If you see Asian tiger mosquitoes, or find any sign of an infestation, you can help to control them by:

* Catching a mosquito in a glass jar and keeping it for examination by the authorities

* In England, reporting any sightings to Public Health England: see www.hpa.org.uk/Topics/InfectiousDiseases/InfectionsAZ/AsianTigerMosquito
email: **mosquito@hpa.org.uk**
and see www.cieh-npap.org/policy.asp (report form provided by the Chartered Institute of Environmental Health)

For more information visit: **www.nonnativespecies.org**
and **www.invasivespeciesireland.com**

© (left) Forestry Commission / (right) Daiju Azuma

ASIAN & CITRUS LONGHORN BEETLES

Anoplophora glabripennis / Anaplophora chinensis

Where does it come from and how can we stop it invading?

Native to China, Japan and Korea, Asian longhorn beetles were introduced to Europe and the USA in packing materials such as wooden pallets, while citrus beetles travel in live trees like bonsai and Japanese maples. In 2012 a breeding population of Asian longhorn beetles was found in Kent: 2,000 trees had to be felled in efforts to eradicate them.

Asian and Citrus longhorn beetles look almost identical: black and shiny, 2.5 to 3cm long, with about 20 irregular white spots on their wing cases, and striped antennae up to twice the length of the body.

Below: Larvae can be up to 5cm long, boring tunnels into trees for up to 3 years, and pupating in chambers sealed with wood shavings.

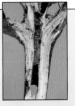

© GBNNSS

What's the problem?

If they became established in Britain and Ireland, Asian and citrus longhorn beetles would pose a major threat to many broadleaved native and forest trees including apple, beech, birch, cherry, hawthorn, hazel, hornbeam, horse chestnut, maple, oak, pear, plane, poplar and willow.

Adult longhorn beetles feed on young bark and fruiting shoots, but larvae cause much more damage by tunnelling under the bark and into the heartwood of affected trees. Often starting on larger branches, larval mines can be up to 1cm in diameter and many centimetres long – killing bark before weakening branches and trunks, and making trees vulnerable to disease and wind damage. Signs of longhorn beetle infestation include bleeding sap where eggs have been laid, rapidly wilting leaves, wood shavings at the entrance of larval mines or around the base of trees, or 1cm 'shot-holes' in tree trunks where adult beetles have emerged in spring.

In Europe, breeding populations of citrus longhorn beetles have already become established in Lombardy, and are now considered ineradicable. Defra's Food and Environment Research Agency (FERA) estimates that controlling a substantial invasion of longhorn beetles in the UK would cost £300 million, with no guarantee of successful eradication

What can I do about it?

As EU-listed pest species, all sightings of Asian and Citrus longhorn beetles **must be urgently reported** to FERA or Invasive Species Ireland. If you see either beetle, or find any signs of an infestation, you can help to control them by:

✳ Catching the beetle in a glass jar and contacting FERA *(see page 4)*

✳ Emailing details and a photograph to
alert_nonnative@ceh.ac.uk

✳ Reporting any sightings to the RISC or Alien Watch recording schemes *(see page 9)*

For more information visit: **www.nonnativespecies.org,
www.forestry.gov.uk/asianlonghornbeetle, www.defra.gov.uk/fera/
asianlonghornbeetle** *and* **www.defra.gov.uk/fera/citruslonghornbeetle**

© GBNNSS

HARLEQUIN LADYBIRD
Harmonia axyridis

Where does it come from and how did it get here?

Also known as multicoloured and Halloween ladybirds, harlequin ladybirds are native to Asia, from Kazakhstan eastward to Korea, Taiwan and Japan. After being introduced to North America as a biological control for aphids, they were first noted in the UK in 2004. In Ireland, 2 colonies were found in 2010.

Invasive harlequin ladybirds are usually red or orange with 15-21 black spots (as above), or black with 2 or 4 orange or red spots (as below). **They are always over 5mm long.**

Native British ladybirds also take several colourations, but are always less than 5mm long.

© Paul Scott

What's the problem?

Harlequin ladybirds are considered the most invasive ladybirds on earth, and extended their range in the UK by 100km per year between 2004 and 2008. During breeding periods they fly strongly, migrating long distances in search of high-density aphid populations. Being larger than many native ladybirds, they also predate voraciously on other species' larval stages, and leave less food for them by reducing overall numbers of aphids. In 2012 a major European study showed that the British native 2-spot ladybird declined by 44% in just 5 years after harlequin ladybirds arrived.

Besides threatening native species, harlequin ladybirds damage orchard crops by feeding on soft fruit when aphids are scarce in late summer and autumn. During winter they hibernate in large numbers inside buildings: if disturbed or crushed, they emit an unpleasant smell and coloured fluid which can stain soft furnishings, and even changes the taste of wine if ladybirds are accidentally harvested with grapes. They may also trigger allergic reactions, and have been reported to bite people in self defence.

What can I do about it?

If you see harlequin ladybirds, you can help to control them by:

* Removing hibernating harlequin ladybirds from a building by securing a nylon stocking inside a vacuum cleaner's hose with a rubber band, before sucking them up into this bag and disposing of them.

* Reporting any sightings to the Harlequin Ladybird Survey at www.harlequin-survey.org

* In Ireland, reporting them to the Alien Watch recording scheme *(see page 9)*

For more information visit: **www.nonnativespecies.org**
www.invasivespeciesireland.com *and* **www.harlequin-survey.org**

© Phil Bendle

NEW ZEALAND FLATWORM
Arthurdendyus triangulates

Where does it come from and how did it get here?

New Zealand flatworms first arrived in the UK and Ireland in the 1960s, probably in soil with specimen plants sent to botanic gardens. By the 1990s there were repeated sightings in Scotland, northern England and Ireland. Similarly voracious Australian flatworms have also been found in south-west England.

Above: New Zealand flatworms are smooth and ribbon-flat, up to 20cm long fully extended, with pointed ends and pale buff-coloured edges and underside. Egg capsules look like blackcurrants in the soil.

Below: Australian flatworms (Australoplana sanguinea) are smaller, pink and oval in cross-section. First recorded in the Scilly Isles in 1980, they have since spread along the south coast of England.

© Ken Harris

What's the problem?

New Zealand flatworms predate heavily on native British earthworms, reducing their numbers to very low levels in affected gardens and farmland. Whilst hunting above and below the surface, flatworms are reportedly capable of reaching speeds of 17m per hour.

Earthworms perform essential ecosystem functions - including soil aeration, assisting decomposition of plant material and even regulating land drainage via their burrows - so these natural processes are interrupted by flatworm predation. Soil fertility is reduced, and native species like moles and badgers are threatened by the loss of an important food source.

What can I do about it?

If you see New Zealand flatworms, or find any signs of an infestation, you can help to control them by:

* Trapping and collecting them under sheets of black polythene. The flatworms will be curled up at rest like tiny swiss rolls: wear gloves for protection against their irritant mucus, and drop them into boiling water to kill them quickly and humanely.

* In Ireland, reporting any sightings to the Alien Watch recording scheme *(see page 9)*

* If you find New Zealand flatworms in your garden, help to stop them spreading by avoiding moving soil, compost or rooted plants from your property. Potted plants from garden centres, friends and relatives are often the source of new infestations. Research from Ireland suggests that any resident flatworms can be killed by standing suspect pots in a warm room (min. 26.5°C) for 24 hours

* Helping native earthworms by placing large plant pots around your garden as 'traps' and inspecting underneath them every few days

© Forestry Commission

OAK PROCESSIONARY MOTH
Thaumetopoea processionea

Where does it come from and how did it get here?

Oak processionary moths have been expanding northwards from central and southern Europe for the last 20 years, and probably reached west London in a shipment of trees for a housing development in 2006. Despite eradication efforts, the moths are steadily extending their range in the UK, with colonies found across south and west London as well as Berkshire.

*Inset left: **Don't touch!** Clustering together or travelling in nose-to-tail processions, these caterpillars are covered in tiny detachable hairs which can cause severe allergic reactions.*

Main picture: Even empty communal nests still contain moulted caterpillar skins and millions of irritating hairs.

Moth

What's the problem?

Oak processionary moth caterpillars can strip leaves from whole oak trees and areas of woodland after hatching in April or May, and are sometimes seen processing across open ground between trees at dawn or dusk. If oaks are in short supply, they feed on beech, birch, hazel, hornbeam and sweet chestnut trees, leaving them equally vulnerable to attack by other pests and diseases.

Apart from damaging trees, oak processionary moth caterpillars present a significant public health risk. Microscopic hairs from older caterpillars carry an allergenic toxin called thaumetopoein, which can cause itchy rashes which last for weeks, breathing problems, anaphylactic shock and even blindness if wind-blown hairs are rubbed into your eyes. Dogs can inhale the hairs, other animals can be affected when browsing under trees containing nests, and small pets have reputedly been seriously affected and even killed.

What can I do about it?

If you see oak processionary moth caterpillars, or find any sign of an infestation including nests, you can help to control them by:

* Reporting them to the Forestry Commission's recording scheme at: www.forestry.gov.uk/opm

* Reporting them to your local council (which may already have set up a task force to handle any infestations)

❗ Hairs from oak processionary moth caterpillars can be transmitted via air, vegetation or water, and remain toxic for up to 5 years. Do not attempt to clear an infestation without professional advice.

Keep children and animals clear: in case of contact with caterpillar hairs, you should seek medical attention immediately (or see a vet if your pet has been affected). Ceterizine-based antihistamine tablets can reduce symptoms of skin irritation.

For more information visit: **www.nonnativespecies.org** *and* **www.forestry.gov.uk/opm**

© Wikispecies / (inset) Ray Dye

RED LILY BEETLE
Lilioceris lilii

Where does it come from and how did it get here?

Native to Eurasia, red or scarlet lily beetles were noticed in the UK at the end of the 19th century.

The first established colony was found in Surrey in 1939, and sightings spread slowly across southern England to cover every county by 2010. Since 2002, these beetles have also been found in Glasgow and Belfast.

Main picture: Red lily beetles are around 8mm long, with bright red wing cases and thorax, and may emit a high-pitched squeal when threatened.

Inset: Juvenile beetles emerge as larvae from April to September, and are usually covered by their own wet black excrement.

What's the problem?

Now becoming widespread across the UK, red lily beetles are increasingly seen as a serious problem for gardeners and horticultural businesses, as well as endangering wild native colonies of the rare wild plants, snakes' head fritillaries.

Adult red lily beetles make round holes in foliage, while juvenile beetles graze on the underside of ornamental lily and fritillary leaves. Damage increases through spring and summer as they move to the tips of the leaves and work back to the stems, rapidly causing severe or total defoliation.

As a result, the plants are unable to draw enough nutrients back down into their bulbs, preventing them from flowering in future years.

What can I do about it?

If you see red lily beetles, or find any signs of an infestation, you can help to control them by:

* Hand picking them off the plants. If you're only growing a few fritillaries or lilies, you may be able to control an infestation of red lily beetles by picking them off the plants every few days before crushing or drowning them in soapy water

* Gardeners in Canada have reported successfully deterring or smothering red lily beetles by covering plants with a thick dusting of talcum powder

* Over wider areas, spraying with a suitable insecticide (recommended by the Royal Horticultural Society)

* In Ireland, reporting any sightings to the Alien Watch recording scheme (*see page 9*)

© Kjetil Lenes

SPANISH SLUG
Arion vulgaris

Where does it come from and how did it get here?

Following much scientific debate (and at least one reclassification), these highly invasive slugs are now thought to have arrived in the UK from the Pyrenees in 1954, and have probably been present in County Antrim in Northern Ireland since 2010. Hybridisation with native slugs could produce a 'super slug' combining extreme voracity with tolerance for cold.

Spanish slugs grow up to 15cm long, with colours varying from orange to greyish-green. In Norway, strawberry-growers have reported losing at least half of their harvest to Spanish slugs.

Bacteria from Spanish slugs may also have caused a Europe-wide E. coli outbreak, linked to cucumbers, lettuce and tomatoes, in 2011.

What's the problem?

Spanish slugs have spread widely via fresh salads, garden centres and the horticultural trade, and are notable for their readiness to colonise man-made habitats, including farming and urban areas. They breed quickly, laying around 400 eggs per year compared to 100 or so laid by other species, and carry a wide range of diseases and parasites to which British slugs and snails have little resistance.

Spanish slugs feed voraciously on a variety of vegetables and ornamental plants, stripping leaves and causing serious damage to gardens and crops across Europe. By producing copious quantities of greenish slime, they can even crawl across dry, sandy soil: cars have reputedly skidded and crashed as a result of large numbers of slugs gathering to feed on others already crushed on roads.

In central Europe, booming sales of slug pellets (to combat this particular species) are thought to have caused toxic bioaccumulation in mollusc-eating birds and animals, as well as dangerous chemicals leaching into water supplies.

What can I do about it?

If you see Spanish slugs, or find any signs of an infestation, you can help to control them by:

* Trapping, collecting and disposing of them by hand (trapping hints can be found on www.slugwatch.co.uk)

* Reporting any sightings to SlugWatch UK at: www.slugwatch.co.uk

* In Ireland, reporting any sightings to the Alien Watch recording scheme *(see page 9)*

Positively identifying Spanish slugs can be difficult even for experts, but a large orange slug 12-15cm long is unlikely to be any other species. Spanish slug mucus is difficult to wash off, and may contain E. coli bacteria: always wear protective gloves when handling Spanish slugs, and drop them into boiling water to kill them quickly and humanely.

For more information visit: **www.invasivespeciesireland.com**
www.nonnativespecies.org, www.cabi.org *and* **www.slugwatch.co.uk**

© John McAvoy

MINK
Neovison vison

Where does it come from and how did it get here?

American mink were brought to Europe for fur farming from the 1920s: the first escaped breeding population in the UK was recorded near Blackpool in 1956. The last fur farm in the UK closed in 2003, but deliberate releases by animal rights activists are still occurring in Ireland. Mink are now almost ubiquitous in Britain, except on some offshore islands.

Above: From the 1920s, mink were widely farmed for their thick, glossy dark brown fur.

Below: In 2002 the Game & Wildlife Conservation Trust pioneered the floating 'mink raft' to detect and trap mink.

© G&WCT

What's the problem?

American mink are highly opportunistic semi-aquatic predators, widely regarded as seriously invasive for their ability to colonise new territories and kill almost every other species including fish, frogs, crayfish, waterfowl and small mammals.

Ground-nesting game and sea birds' eggs and chicks are very vulnerable to mink, and they've had a devastating effect on water voles in many parts of the UK. Mink are small enough to chase them all the way into their burrows, and water vole populations have crashed by 95% since the 1950s. Experts agree that mink need to be eradicated before any reintroduction of water voles can take place in areas suffering from these local extinctions. Some evidence also suggests that mink are declining in regions where native otters are making a comeback.

What can I do about it?

If you're the landowner, or have the landowner's permission, you can help to control mink all year round by:

* Shooting humanely with a licensed firearm (if in doubt, get training first)
* Trapping and shooting humanely in the trap, which should be inspected at least once a day. Avoid ricochets by placing the trap on soft ground
* In Ireland, reporting any sightings to the Alien Watch recording scheme *(see page 9)*

Mink often travel along river corridors, so monitoring and follow-up trapping have proved very effective in control programmes in Scotland, Herefordshire and elsewhere. Use a damp clay pad (inspected every week or so) in a tunnel on a floating 'mink raft' to detect mink, then add a cage trap to the tunnel.

It is illegal to release captured mink. Drowning is considered to be inhumane.

For more information visit: www.nonnativespecies.org
www.naturalengland.org.uk, www.invasivespeciesireland.com
www.gwct.org.uk *and* www.scottishmink.org.uk

© GE/VVSS

BROWN RAT
Rattus norwegicus

Where does it come from and how did it get here?

Brown rats are believed to have evolved on the central Asian steppes, and reached Europe in the early 1770s. Moving along human trade routes and travelling as stowaways on ships, they were first noted in English ports in 1728. They have since become widespread in the UK, except on a few remote islands and exposed upland areas, as well as worldwide.

Brown rats can be distinguished from other mammals such as water voles by their large size and long, thin, almost hairless tail.

On islands like South Georgia, the Scilly Isles and Rathlin Island, conservationists hope that eradicating brown rats will save endangered seabird colonies.

What's the problem?

Brown rats are considered one of the world's worst invasive species – damaging property, causing economic and public health problems including contamination of stored food, and driving other species into extinction. They breed quickly, swim well, foul more food than they eat, and proliferate around human settlements. They also carry several dangerous pathogens including *cryptosporidiosis, toxiplasmosis, listeriosis* and *leptospirosis* (Weil's disease), all of which can severely affect people's or farm animals' health.

By predating on huge numbers of other species, brown rats cause serious damage to biodiversity and the natural balance of whole ecosystems – particularly on islands where they've caused or accelerated many extinctions or near-extinctions of native species. Ground-nesting seabird colonies, especially their eggs and chicks, are particularly vulnerable. On the Galapagos Islands, rats are believed to have killed every tortoise hatchling for the past 100 years.

What can I do about it?

If you're the landowner, or have the landowner's permission, you can help to control brown rats all year round by:

* Shooting humanely with an air rifle or licensed firearm

* Trapping and dispatching humanely: cage traps or snares should be inspected at least once a day. Trapped rats should be run into a sack, gripped with thick gloves and killed with a sharp blow to the head, or by shot in the cage with a suitable weapon

* Reducing the amount of cover for rats around farm buildings

* Warfarin poison baiting following guidelines from the Campaign for Responsible Rodenticide Use (www.thinkwildlife.org)

For more information visit: **www.nonnativespecies.org** *and* **www.basc.org.uk**

© GBNNSS

CANADA GOOSE

Branta canadensis

Where does it come from and how did it get here?

First brought to St James' Park in London as an ornamental attraction around 1665, Canada geese didn't become widespread in the British Isles until the 1950s. Since then, their numbers have boomed as a result of deliberate dispersal for sporting purposes, as well as the creation of vast new tracts of suitable habitat in flooded sand and gravel pits.

Canada geese prefer slow-flowing freshwater or lakes, with plenty of suitable grazing nearby.

During nesting season, adult birds behave aggressively towards people and dogs.

What's the problem?

From around 4,000 in the 1950s, the UK's population of Canada geese is now up to 100,000. They thrive in proximity to human settlements, taking full advantage of golf courses, urban parks and farmland near lakes and waterways. Large flocks foul parks, footpaths and sports fields with slippery bacteria-laden droppings: they also destroy pastures, crops, flower beds and waterside vegetation, and can cause eutrophication of small lakes and streams.

Maybe most seriously, Canada geese have been implicated in thousands of bird strikes on aircraft worldwide, including multiple engine failure on a Concorde in 1995: experts suggest it's only a matter of time before a major aviation disaster is caused in the British Isles.

What can I do about it?

If you're the landowner, or have the landowner's permission, you can help to control Canada geese by:

* Shooting humanely with a licensed firearm during your local legal open season. Under the terms and conditions of Natural England's general licences, you may also be able to shoot Canada geese during their normal closed season

* Pricking or painting eggs with liquid paraffin (with appropriate permissions). If you can locate all your local nests (up to 600m from water!) throughout the nesting season, egg pricking is considered to be effective and humane

* Rounding up flocks of geese during the flightless period in June and July, and dispatching them humanely

* Fencing off islands or access to the water's edge, and discouraging feeding by the public

* In Ireland, reporting any sightings to the Alien Watch recording scheme (see page 9)

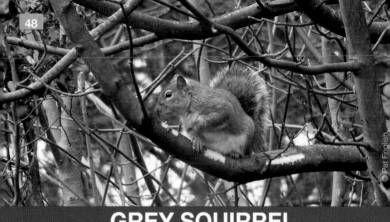

© Pat Frolish

GREY SQUIRREL

Sciurus carolinensis

Where does it come from and how did it get here?

Native to eastern areas of North America, from Texas and Florida north to Quebec, Britain's first grey squirrels were introduced to parkland in Denbighshire (Wales) as fashionable novelties in 1828. Further releases took place in Cheshire and elsewhere between 1876 and 1929. Grey squirrels are now widespread across the British Isles.

Many grey squirrel populations developed from fewer than 10 original squirrels released by Victorian landowners.

Thanks to successful clearance of grey squirrels, refuges for threatened red squirrels have been recreated on Anglesey and in Cornwall.

What's the problem?

Grey squirrels carry squirrel parapox virus, which is deadly to red squirrels (and may also be transmissible to humans). As a result of this disease, plus competition for food, grey squirrels cause extinction of red squirrels wherever they come into contact. In 2012 it was estimated that there were more than 2.5 million grey squirrels in Britain, compared to just 120,000 reds, mostly in Scotland.

Grey squirrels cause at least £50 million damage every year to commercial forestry and ancient woodlands, killing and stunting trees by stripping bark for food and territorial displays. Research by the Game & Wildlife Conservation Trust also suggests that songbird populations may suffer from serious nest predation in areas with high numbers of grey squirrels.

What can I do about it?

If you're the landowner, or have the landowner's permission, you can help to control grey squirrels all year round by:

* Shooting humanely with an air rifle or licensed firearm

* Trapping and dispatching humanely: traps should be inspected at least once a day

* Warfarin poison baiting under guidelines from the Campaign for Responsible Rodenticide Use (www.thinkwildlife.org)

* Single catch live-capture cage traps are thought to be the most effective trapping method, baited with peanuts and/or whole yellow maize.

It is illegal to release captured grey squirrels. Trapped squirrels should be humanely dispatched: either by running into a sack, gripping with thick gloves and killing with a sharp blow to the head, or by shooting in the cage with a suitable weapon, avoiding ricochets by placing the trap on soft ground. Drowning is considered to be inhumane.

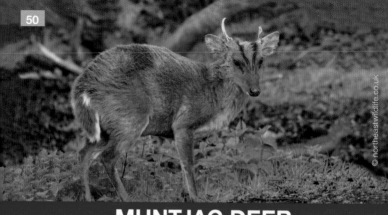

© northeastwildlife.co.uk

MUNTJAC DEER
Muntiacus reevesi

Where does it come from and how did it get here?

Also known as barking deer, muntjac were introduced to the UK from their native south east China and Taiwan as an exotic addition to the deer park at Bedfordshire's Woburn Abbey in 1901. They began to breed in captivity, escaped during the 1920s, and have now spread through southern England and Wales as far north as Yorkshire. Small numbers have been seen in Ireland.

Muntjac are the smallest deer in the UK, measuring just 50cm high at the shoulder.

With distinctive dark facial markings, a muntjac can sometimes be mistaken for a large dog like an Alsatian.

What's the problem?

Muntjac numbers in the UK have exploded from around 2,000 to more than 2 million since 1963. With few natural predators to control them, they are now regarded as an increasingly serious threat to ancient woodlands where high concentrations of these deer cause extensive damage to trees and iconic native species like bluebells, dormice and nightingales. According to the RSPB, deer damage to undergrowth may be one of the most important factors in the decline of ground-nesting birds. Much to the chagrin of gardeners, they're also particularly fond of rose bushes, incurring huge fencing and other costs for land managers.

One of the oldest known species of deer, muntjac are armed with unusual tusks as well as small antlers, and have been been known to attack dogs and even people when startled or defending their young. They're also a night-time hazard on British roads, where they wander into the path of cars and may cause up to 40,000 traffic accidents every year.

What can I do about it?

If you're the landowner, or have the landowner's permission, you can help to control muntjac deer all year round by:

* Shooting humanely with a suitably powerful licensed firearm. Because of their ability to breed at any time of the year, there's no legal close season during which muntjac may not be shot. However, BASC recommends avoiding shooting female muntjac unless they are either immature, or heavily pregnant with no fawn at heel, to avoid orphaning dependent young. Alternatively, you may wish to consult a licensed stalker

* Reporting any sightings to the RISC or Alien Watch recording schemes (see page 9)

© northeastwildlife.co.uk

RABBIT
Oryctolagus cuniculus

Where does it come from and how did it get here?

Some evidence suggests that rabbits inhabited Britain during the last interglacial period, but they were reintroduced to the UK mainland from continental Europe by the Normans some time before 1235. Farmed in heavily-guarded warrens as a valuable source of food and fur, they soon escaped and are now naturalised throughout the UK and Ireland.

Most of Britain's rabbits were killed by viral myxomatosis in the 1950s, but numbers have now bounced back to more than 45 million.

Rabbits are estimated to cause over £100 million of agricultural damage every year in the UK alone.

What's the problem?

As one of Britain's most recognisable small mammals, rabbits have lots of cultural significance, appearing in children's literature as diverse as Lewis Carroll's *Alice's Adventures in Wonderland*, Beatrix Potter's *Peter Rabbit* and *The Tale of the Flopsy Bunnies*, and JK Rowling's *Tales of Beedle the Bard*.

However, Defra also considers them the UK's costliest INNS, causing £263 million of damage to gardens, grassland, crops and trees every year. Rabbits multiply rapidly: a doe can become pregnant again one day after giving birth, and her litter of 3–6 kittens can start breeding themselves at an age of just 4 months. By grazing small plants and de-barking saplings up to a height of 50cm from the ground, rabbits kill trees and prevent woodland regeneration on a landscape scale: they're a key food source for mink, and help invasive Hottentot figs to spread in coastal areas. Horses and other livestock can also be injured by stumbling into rabbit burrows.

On the other hand, rabbits are important prey for native predators and scavengers like buzzards, red kites, foxes, stoats and polecats. Long-term naturalisation also means they've altered and maintained many ecosystems in favour of endangered species like stone curlew and large blue butterflies.

More than 95% of the UK's rabbits were killed by the deliberate introduction of *myxomatosis* from Uruguay and France in the 1950s, but the population now appears to be increasing by about 2% per year.

What can I do about it?

If you're the landowner, or have the landowner's permission, you can help to control rabbits all year round by:

* Shooting humanely with an air rifle or licensed firearm

* Trapping and dispatching humanely: cage traps or snares should be inspected at least once a day

© GBNNSS

RING-NECKED & MONK PARAKEETS

Psittacula krameri, Myiopsitta monachus

Where does it come from and how did it get here?

Popular urban myths suggest that south west London's ring-necked parakeets originated from a pair released by Jimi Hendrix in Carnaby Street in the 1960s, or even escaped from the African Queen film set at Shepperton Studios. However, they probably arrived from central Africa via India and the pet trade: the current breeding populations date from 1969.

Above left: Often drawing attention to themselves with loud, screeching calls, ring-necked parakeets are native to central Africa and India.

Above right: South American monk parakeets (Myiopsitta monachus) are also present in isolated colonies, and are subject to active control by Defra.

What's the problem?

The UK's population of ring-necked parakeets appears to be growing at a rate of up to 30% a year, and is expanding across London and other areas including Manchester. In south London, they've chewed through wood-shingled church roofs and spires to nest inside, while studies in Belgium suggest that they outcompete native birds like nuthatches for tree cavity nesting sites. They damage commercial and garden crops, stripping fruit from trees and vines, and have reputedly reduced grape yields at Painshill vineyard in Surrey by up to 90%, resulting in the loss of thousands of bottles of wine.

In other countries, monk parakeets also cause major economic and infrastructure problems by building car-sized nests on electricity pylons, shorting-out cables and causing fires and blackouts when the nests get soaked with rain. Both species can affect peoples' health by transmitting *psittacosis* bacteria, as well as poultry diseases, and cause extensive fouling under large communal roosts.

What can I do about it?

If you're the landowner, or have the landowner's permission, and parakeets are causing significant damage to crops or native wildlife, you can help to control them by:

* Shooting humanely with a licensed firearm (under general licence from Natural England, like pigeons, crows or magpies)

* Cage-trapping and dispatching humanely: traps should be inspected at least once a day

* In Ireland, reporting any sightings to the Alien Watch recording scheme *(see page 9)*

If you want to keep parakeets or other non-native birds and animals as pets, you can still help to stop them escaping by following the Be Pet Wise guidelines on page 95. Allowing them to escape is an offence.

For more information visit: **www.nonnativespecies.org**
www.naturalengland.org.uk *and* **www.invasivespeciesireland.com**

© northeastwildlife.co.uk

SIKA DEER
Cervus nippon

Where does it come from and how did it get here?

Native to south east Asia, sika deer were introduced to the UK in 1860, with further movement and releases into deer parks in England and Scotland until 1930. In 1899 they were introduced to the Powerscourt estate in Wicklow, and escaped into the wild during political unrest in the 1920s. They have since spread to Wexford, Kildare and Carlow.

Sika can easily be confused with native British red deer, especially since many populations now contain hybrids of both species. During the rut, sika stags vocalise with a long-drawn-out siren-like call, rather than the classic red deer bellow.

What's the problem?

Since the Victorian era, sika deer have shown an unexpected ability to interbreed freely with native British red deer – to such an extent that scientists now believe that up to 40% of all deer in Scotland may already be fertile sika/red deer hybrids. As such, there's a real risk that genetically pure red deer could become extinct on the Scottish mainland, although ark sites on remote islands could be protected or even created by eradicating sika and hybrid deer first.

Apart from this genetic threat, sika deer damage commercial forestry by using their antlers to leave distinctive vertical scars in mature tree trunks as a territorial advertisement during the breeding season. They also threaten regeneration of native woodlands by stripping bark with their teeth and browsing the leader shoots of young trees.

In Killarney, sika deer have benefited from cover provided by thickets of invasive Pontic rhododendron *(see page 18)*.

What can I do about it?

If you're the landowner, or have the landowner's permission, you can help to control sika deer at certain times of the year by:

* Shooting humanely with a suitably powerful licensed firearm during your local legal open season

* In Ireland, reporting any sightings to the Alien Watch recording scheme *(see page 9)*

Sika deer are protected by an annual close season: shooting dates vary for stags and hinds in different parts of the UK and Ireland, so you're strongly recommended to consult the BASC or your relevant regulatory body to check which dates may apply in your area. Alternatively, you may wish to consult a licensed stalker.

© GBNNSS

AUSTRALIAN SWAMP STONECROP
Crassula helmsii

Where does it come from and how did it get here?

Also known as New Zealand pigmyweed, Australian swamp stonecrop was brought to Britain from Tasmania in 1911 as an oxygenating plant for ponds and aquaria. First recorded in the wild in Essex in 1956, and in Armagh in 1984, it is still spreading.

Main picture: Australian swamp stonecrop grows in dense mats or light green tussocks, with fleshy leaves in opposite pairs, each up to 2cm long.

Unlike starwort, which is native to the UK, Australian swamp stonecrop has no notch at the end of each leaf (see inset).

What's the problem?

Australian swamp stonecrop grows vigorously all year round in still or slow-moving water, forming dense impenetrable mats of vegetation which out-compete all other native water plants. It tolerates a wide range of pH values, including slightly salty water, and can also colonise damp mud in ditches and the drawdown edges of reservoirs.

Since it can form a new plant from a single node on a 1cm fragment of stem, Australian swamp stonecrop spreads easily on boats, clothing and possibly even wildfowl. Some new introductions may still be occurring as a result of people discarding pond and aquarium plants.

What can I do about it?

Planting or otherwise causing Australian swamp stonecrop to grow in the wild is against the law in the UK and Ireland. From April 2014, it's also banned from sale in England and Wales. With the landowner's permission, you can help to control it by:

* Shading it out with black polythene for at least 3 months during the growing season

* Filling in the infested pond and digging a new one nearby

* Reporting any sightings to Ireland's Alien Watch recording scheme, or the UK's PlantTracker app *(see page 9)*

If your pond contains Australian swamp stonecrop, or you take part in water-based activities such as fishing, canoeing or sailing on a water body where it's present, you can help to stop it spreading further by following the Check-Clean-Dry and Be Plant Wise biosecurity guidelines *(see pages 94-95)*. Check for even the smallest fragments sticking to your boots, clothing, boat bilges and other sporting equipment, then clean your kit with clean water and dry it thoroughly before using it at another location.

For more information visit: **www.nonnativespecies.org**
www.environment-agency.gov.uk

© Joel Caffrey (IFI)

CURLY-LEAVED WATERWEED
Lagarosiphon major

Where does it come from and how did it get here?

Curly-leaved waterweed is native to southern Africa, and was first noted growing wild in the UK in a Hertfordshire gravel pit in 1944, having been introduced as an oxygenating pond or aquarium plant. Now spreading north across the British Isles, it has also become particularly problematic in Ireland's Lough Corrib.

Above: The devastating effect of this weed choking a previously clear bay in Lough Corrib. Curly-leaved waterweed grows from the bed upwards to form a dense canopy of vegetation across the surface.

Below: Leaves grow in curved spirals around long, brittle stems: fragments break off easily, sink, and root to establish new colonies.

© GBNNSS

What's the problem?

Curly-leaved waterweed can grow in water up to 6m deep, spreading profusely in still or slow-moving water.

Dense growth of curly-leaved waterweed crowds out native plants, reduces biodiversity, causes major fluctuations in water oxygenation, and disrupts sailing, fishing and other sports. In stormy weather, large amounts of vegetation break off and wash up onto beaches in smelly rotting piles, making the shoreline an unpleasant place to visit.

What can I do about it?

Planting or otherwise causing curly-leaved waterweed to grow in the wild is against the law in the UK and Ireland. From April 2014, it's also banned from sale in England and Wales. With the landowner's permission, you can help to control it by:

* Shading it out with a biodegradable natural fabric such as jute matting

* Reporting any sightings to Ireland's Alien Watch recording scheme, or the UK's PlantTracker app *(see page 9)*

Since 2009, Inland Fisheries Ireland has successfully tested jute matting to suppress curly-leaved waterweed on 20,000 m/sq of Lough Corrib. Jute matting saturates and sinks readily, and forms a stable substrate for native plants before eventually biodegrading completely. Curly-leaved waterweed dies and decays within 4 months of the durable matting being laid over it, while indigenous species can regrow through the open weave.

You can help to stop it spreading further by following the Check-Clean-Dry and Be Plant Wise biosecurity guidelines *(see pages 94-95)*. Check for even the smallest fragments sticking to your boots, clothing, boat bilges and other sporting equipment, then clean your kit with clean water and dry it thoroughly before using it at another location.

For more information visit: **www.nonnativespecies.org** **www.environment-agency.gov.uk, www.invasivespeciesireland.com** *and* **www.fisheriesireland.ie**

© GBNNSS

FLOATING PENNYWORT

Hydrocotyle ranunculoides

Where does it come from and how did it get here?

Native to Africa and the Americas, floating pennywort is threatened in parts of its original range in the USA, but is spreading rapidly north and west from southern counties of the UK. It was introduced in the 1980s as an ornamental plant for tropical aquaria and garden ponds, and was first noted in the wild in Essex in 1990.

Main picture: Floating pennywort forms green mats spreading out from the banks of slow-flowing canals or rivers.

Inset: This plant can be identified by its fleshy horizontal stems and lobed, circular, or kidney shaped leaves.

What's the problem?

By anchoring itself to the bank, floating pennywort spreads in densely interwoven mats of fleshy leaves and stems across the surface of slow-flowing or still water, growing at a rate of 20cm per day.

It shades out native plants, damages underwater ecosystems, restricts navigation, and causes serious flood risks. In the UK, the official cost of herbicide control is already £250,000 to £300,000 per year.

What can I do about it?

Planting or causing floating pennywort to grow in the wild is against the law in the UK and Ireland. From April 2014, it's also banned from sale in England and Wales. With the landowner's permission, you can help to control it by:

* Pulling it out of the water and leaving it on the bank to compost. Regular pulling (May–October) helps to prevent floating pennywort from achieving total dominance. Complete new plants can grow from small pieces of stem, which snap off easily, so all fragments of broken vegetation should be carefully netted out of the water

* Spraying with glyphosate in winter, when it dies back between growing seasons (regulatory approval will be required, as well as pre-spraying the waxy leaves with surfactant to help the herbicide stick to them)

* Reporting any sightings to the Alien Watch recording scheme, or the UK's PlantTracker app *(see page 9)*

You can help to stop it spreading further by following the Check-Clean-Dry and Be Plant Wise biosecurity guidelines *(see pages 94-95)*. Check for even the smallest fragments sticking to your boots, clothing, boat bilges and other sporting equipment, then clean your kit with clean water and dry it thoroughly before using it at another location.

For more information visit: **www.nonnativespecies.org** **www.environment-agency.gov.uk** *and* **www.invasivespeciesireland.com**

PARROT'S FEATHER
Myriophyllum aquaticum

Where does it come from and how did it get here?

Also known as Brazilian water milfoil, parrot's feather has been grown in British water gardens since 1878. Probably after being discarded as garden waste, it was first found growing wild in the England in 1960, followed by Ireland in 1990. Its native range is the Amazon basin, but it has now escaped and become naturalised on every continent except Antarctica.

Main picture: Parrot's feather has plumed blue-green leaves in 4 to 6 whorls around fleshy, brittle green stems.

Inset: When the stems emerge above the water's surface, they can grow up to 30cm high, looking like small fir trees, sometimes with pink flowers.

What's the problem?

Parrot's feather is usually found in still or slow flowing nutrient-rich water, where it forms thick mats on the surface, shading out native plants and algae beneath. Like many other invasive species, it has the ability to root new plants from tiny fragments of stem.

Parrot's feather quickly chokes water – entangling swimmers and boat propellers, clogging drainage channels, increasing the risk of flooding, and creating ideal breeding conditions for mosquitoes.

What can I do about it?

Planting or otherwise causing parrot's feather to grow in the wild is against the law in the UK and Ireland. From April 2014, it's also banned from sale in England and Wales. With the landowner's permission, you can help to control it by:

* Pulling stems by hand to clear small colonies *(see below)*

* Shading it out with black polythene during the growing season

* Spraying with glyphosate (regulatory approval will be required, as well as pre-spraying the waxy emergent 'feathers' with surfactant to help the herbicide stick to them)

* Reporting any sightings to the Alien Watch recording scheme, or the UK's PlantTracker app *(see page 9)*

All fragments of cut vegetation should be carefully netted, removed and composted to prevent regrowth. If your pond contains parrot's feather, or you take part in water-based activities, you can help to stop it spreading further by following the Check-Clean-Dry and Be Plant Wise biosecurity guidelines *(see pages 94-95)*. Check for even the smallest fragments sticking to your boots, clothing, boat bilges and other sporting equipment, then clean your kit with clean water and dry it thoroughly before using it at another location.

For more information visit: **www.nonnativespecies.org**
www.environment-agency.gov.uk *and* **www.invasivespeciesireland.com**

© GBNNS

WATER FERN
Azolla filiculoides

Where does it come from and how did it get here?

Sometimes called floating fairy fern, *Azolla filiculoides* was brought to Britain from its native range in tropical America as an ornamental plant for ponds and aquaria. Still the only floating fern in the UK and Ireland, it was first found growing in the wild in 1883, and has spread especially quickly in the last 50 years.

Water fern usually forms a green carpet over still water, but can turn red in response to stress like winter cold, bright sunlight or brackish water.

Azolla filiculoides is a small, free-floating mini fern just 2.5cm across, with scale-like leaves and roots hanging into the water.

What's the problem?

In warm conditions, water fern can double its biomass every 2-3 days, spreading by spores and forming dense mats of foliage which shade out submerged oxygenating plants, which reduces water quality and can even lead to fish kills. (49 million years ago, 800,000 years of *Azolla* blooms in the freshwater Atlantic ocean sequestered up to 80% of Earth's carbon dioxide – leading to global cooling and ice-caps at both poles for the first time in our planet's history).

Since the surface of a waterway covered by water fern appears solid, it can also create a safety hazard for unwary people and animals.

What can I do about it?

Planting or otherwise causing water fern to grow in the wild is against the law in the UK and Ireland. From April 2014, it's also banned from sale in England and Wales. With the landowner's permission, you can help to control it by:

* Taking careful biosecurity measures when leaving an infected area to avoid taking tiny plants with you
* Working with a local action group to introduce *Stenopelmus rufinasus* weevils as a biological control
* Pulling by hand, or scooping it off the surface of the water with a net *(see below)*
* Reporting any sightings to the RISC or Alien Watch recording schemes, or the UK's PlantTracker app *(see page 9)*

On larger ponds, use a pump to spray pond water and push water fern to the edge for netting out. All fragments should be carefully removed and composted. If your pond contains water fern, or you take part in water-based activities, prevent further spread by following the Check-Clean-Dry and Be Plant Wise biosecurity guidelines *(see pages 94-95)*. Check for even the smallest fragments sticking to your sporting equipment, then clean your kit with clean water and dry it thoroughly before using it at another location.

For more information visit: **www.nonnativespecies.org** www.environment-agency.gov.uk *and* www.invasivespeciesireland.com

© GBNNSS

WATER PRIMROSE
Ludwigia spp

Where does it come from and how did it get here?

Several species of invasive water primrose have been introduced to Europe from South America as ornamental plants. In the UK, more than a dozen escapee colonies have already been identified and targeted for eradication (including a colony at the London Wetland Centre in Barnes, London).

Main picture: Leaves are generally willow-like, dark green with a paler central rib, and alternating on stems 20-300cm long.

Inset: Water primrose has bright yellow flowers with 5 petals.

What's the problem?

If water primrose were to become established in the UK, the estimated cost to the economy would be more than £150 million each year.

Water primrose spreads out from the banks of slow-flowing rivers or stillwaters, forming thick carpets of vegetation across the water which quickly out-compete native species and increase the risk of flooding by choking drainage channels. In France, Holland and Belgium, controlling water primrose costs several million euros annually. Early season leaves are rounded and curled *(see main picture)*. Later in the year, when the yellow flowers appear, leaves above water-level become slender and pointed, like willow leaves *(see inset)*.

What can I do about it?

Planting or otherwise causing water primrose to grow in the wild is against the law in the UK and Ireland. From April 2014, it's also banned from sale in England and Wales. With the landowner's permission, you can help to control it by:

* Pulling stems by hand to clear small colonies

* Cutting or raking every 6-9 weeks during the growing season to weaken a larger infestation

* In the UK, emailing details and a photograph to **alert_nonnative@ceh.ac.uk** if you find it growing in the wild

* Reporting any sightings to the RISC or Alien Watch recording schemes, or the UK's PlantTracker app *(see page 9)*

If you want to keep water primrose as an ornamental plant in your garden, you can still help to stop it escaping by following the Check-Clean-Dry and Be Plant Wise biosecurity guidelines *(see pages 94-95)*. In particular, remove and compost any cuttings carefully, and prevent it from spreading beyond your own property.

© GBNNSS

AMERICAN BULLFROG

Lithobates catesbeianus

Where does it come from and how did it get here?

American bullfrogs are native to the eastern USA but have been introduced to many other countries as unwanted pets, escapees from garden ponds, or as a biological control for insect pests. They were first recorded in the wild in the UK in 1996 in East Sussex.

American bullfrogs draw attention to themselves with loud, roaring calls from March to October, and hibernate underwater through the winter.

Bullfrogs grow up to 20cm long, twice the size of native British frogs: tadpoles are also unusually large, up to 15cm long.

What's the problem?

American bullfrogs have been found in only a few locations in the UK, but they're considered a serious enough threat to native biodiversity to be the official subject of targeted eradication (the first population in East Sussex was successfully eradicated after the removal of at least 9,000 bullfrogs).

Bullfrogs predate heavily on other species of frogs, toads, newts, fish, small mammals and even ducklings. Most seriously, they can also carry the infectious chytrid fungus and spread fatal *chytridiomycosis* to native British amphibians: this disease has contributed to dramatic population declines and even extinctions of amphibians across the world *(see page 88)*.

So far, more than £100,000 has been spent on monitoring and controlling American bullfrogs in the UK.

What can I do about it?

If you see American bullfrogs, or find any sign of an infestation, you can help to control them by:

* Taking careful biosecurity measures when you leave the area *(see below and pages 94-95)*

* Reporting any sightings to the RISC or Alien Watch recording schemes *(see page 9)*

If you take part in water-based activities such as fishing, canoeing or sailing on a water body where bullfrogs are present, you can help to stop them spreading further by following the Check-Clean-Dry biosecurity guidelines *(see page 94)*.

If you want to keep non-native frogs or other amphibians as pets, you can still help stop to them escaping and possibly becoming invasive by following the Be Pet Wise guidelines on page 95.

© Trevor Renals (inset) / GBNNSS

AMERICAN SIGNAL CRAYFISH
Pacifastacus leniusculus

Where does it come from and how did it get here?

American signal crayfish are native to the Klamath River drainage in California, where ironically they may now be endangered. They were introduced to Sweden in 1959, and transferred to English fish farms in 1975, from which they've spread widely and rapidly via accidental escapes and deliberate introductions. They were first recorded in Scotland in 1995.

Main picture: American signal crayfish look like small, reddish-brown lobsters.

The underside of their claws is bright 'signal' red, with a white or turquoise blotch at its hinge (below).

Other invasive crayfish include Louisiana red swamp crayfish, which have bitten swimmers in London's Hampstead Heath ponds.

What's the problem?

Invasive crayfish are one of the greatest threats to freshwater ecosystems worldwide. In the UK, American signal crayfish are rapidly driving native white-clawed crayfish into extinction – both by outcompeting them with larger size and faster growth rates, and because signal crayfish can carry crayfish plague, which is lethal to white-clawed crayfish.

American signal crayfish also devastate the wider environment, reducing overall invertebrate biomass in infested waters by more than 40%. By undermining banks with half-moon-shaped tunnels up to 2m long, they increase erosion and dump silt into gravels, which inhibits successful spawning by native fish. Recent research by the Ribble Rivers Trust shows that they drive trout and other fish out of streambed refuges into areas where they're more vulnerable to predation. Signal crayfish may also be responsible for the decline of many amphibians.

What can I do about it?

If you see American signal or other alien crayfish, or find any sign of an infestation, you can help to control them by:

* If you catch an alien crayfish, it's illegal to release it or allow it to escape: crushing is usually the easiest and most humane means of dispatch

* Taking careful biosecurity measures when you leave the area *(see page 94)*

* Reporting any sightings to the RISC or Alien Watch recording schemes *(see page 9)*

In England and Wales, Environment Agency consent is required to trap any crayfish: some research suggests that very intensive trapping can reduce infestations, but there's still no reliable control for American signal crayfish except stringent biosecurity and stopping them reaching your water in the first place.

For more information visit: **www.nonnativespecies.org**
www.environment-agency.gov.uk *and* **www.invasivespeciesireland.com**

© National Oceanic and Atmospheric Administration

BLOODY-RED MYSID
Hemimysis anomala

Where does it come from and how did it get here?

From their native Ponto-Caspian region, bloody-red mysids spread across mainland Europe via canals, rivers and intentional introductions as fish food. First recorded in the UK in 2004 at the international water sports centre on the Trent, they've also appeared in Rutland Water and other reservoirs, and reached Ireland's Lough Derg and Shannon system in 2008.

Main picture: Bloody-red mysids are shrimp-like crustaceans, 6-11mm long, which brood their young in pouches and range from deep red to yellow in colour.

They avoid direct sunlight, but migrate to the water's surface in the evening in huge red 'blooms', often around marinas and jetties.

What's the problem?

Although bloody-red mysids were deliberately distributed around the former USSR to boost fish stocks with better feeding, evidence suggests that this produced little benefit and may have damaged many ecosystems beyond repair.

Bloody-red mysids can breed rapidly, live under ice, tolerate wide ranges of salinity, and even survive complete changes of ships' ballast water. They form huge colonies and alter whole food webs by feeding heavily on zooplankton. As a result, essential food supplies for fish are actually reduced overall, while nutrient levels in the water increase as a result of the mysids' massive faecal input.

Any contaminants are likely to biomagnify up the extended food chain, which may affect people's health if they eat fish from water colonised by bloody-red mysids.

What can I do about it?

If you see bloody-red mysids, or find any sign of an infestation, you can help to control them by:

* Taking careful biosecurity measures when you leave the area *(see below and page 94)*

* Reporting any sightings to the RISC or Alien Watch recording schemes *(see page 9)*

If you take part in water-based activities such as fishing, canoeing or sailing on a water body where bloody-red mysids are present, you can help to stop them spreading further by following the Check-Clean-Dry biosecurity guidelines *(see page 94)*. Bloody-red mysids may have reached the UK's Holme Pierrepont international water sports centre via boating equipment.

Apart from stringent biosecurity measures, no effective means of control are currently known.

For more information visit: **www.nonnativespecies.org,** **www.invasivespeciesireland.com** *and* **www.habitas.org.uk/invasive**

© GBNNSS

CARPET SEA SQUIRT
Didemnum vexillum

Where does it come from and how did it get here?

Carpet sea squirts were first confirmed in British waters in 2008, probably having arrived from Japan via boating marinas in France. They have now been recorded in at least 10 ports and marinas around the British Isles, including the Dart, Solent and Clyde as well as intertidal oyster trestles in Galway Bay.

Main picture: Carpet sea squirts are colony-living marine filter-feeding animals which hang like carpets of dripping candle wax from hard surfaces like docks and ship's hulls (see below). By smothering shellfish beds, they can damage native reefs and the fishing industry.

© Notice Nature

What's the problem?

Carpet sea squirts attach themselves to hard surfaces and infrastructure including docks, boats and shellfish farming equipment, quickly forming large colonies which carpet these structures and smother native oysters, mussels and other bivalves.

As such, carpet sea squirts have potential to cause severe damage to native reefs and gravel habitats as well as national fishing industries. If they spread as widely in British waters as they've already done in New Zealand and the USA, it's estimated that they could cost mussel farmers between £1.3 and £6.8 million over the next ten years. In North America's Puget Sound, control measures have already added up to $750,000 US.

What can I do about it?

If you see carpet sea squirts, or find any sign of an infestation, you can help to control them by:

* Taking careful biosecurity measures when you leave the area *(see below and page 94)*
* Emailing details and a photograph to: **alert_nonnative@ceh.ac.uk**
* Reporting any sightings to the RISC or Alien Watch recording schemes *(see page 9)*
* If you find carpet sea squirts attached to your boat, Invasive Species Ireland recommends dry docking the vessel without dislodging them, before high-pressure hosing with fresh water, and drying for at least 48 hours. All washings off the boat should be carefully contained and disposed of, not allowed to escape back into the marine environment. Before re-floating your boat, anti-fouling paint should be re-applied

If you take part in marine water-based activities, you can help to stop carpet sea squirts spreading further by following the Check-Clean-Dry biosecurity guidelines *(see page 94)*.

For more information visit: **www.nonnativespecies.org**
www.environment-agency.gov.uk *and* **www.invasivespeciesireland.com**

© GBNNSS

CHINESE MITTEN CRAB
Ericocheir sinensis

Where does it come from and how did it get here?

Chinese mitten crabs are valued as a delicacy in their native range, and probably spread from Korea and the Yellow Sea by stowing away in ships' ballast water. They've been present in the Thames since 1935, with later colonies in the Humber, Medway, Ouse, Tyne, Tamar, Waterford, Suir and Barrow estuaries, and have also been found in Southfields reservoir in Yorkshire.

Chinese mitten crabs can be distinguished by a dense mat of hair on their white-tipped claws.

By burrowing deep tunnels into river banks, mitten crabs increase flood risk and erosion, especially in tidal areas.

What's the problem?

Chinese mitten crabs have potential to cause huge economic and environmental damage across the UK and Ireland. Migrating slowly upstream from their breeding grounds in brackish estuarine waters, they dig burrows up to 1m long into soft river banks and levees - increasing flood risk and erosion, and incurring huge costs for repairing collapsing flood defences. They can also walk long distances across dry land to bypass obstructions or colonise new river systems.

Chinese mitten crabs predate voraciously on a wide variety of aquatic insects and fish eggs, and may be able to out-compete native species like white-clawed crayfish, while silt from banks they've undermined makes water murky and clogs gravels where native fish spawn. Mitten crabs also carry diseases and parasites including the Oriental lung fluke, which can affect humans if the crabs aren't well cooked before being eaten.

What can I do about it?

If you see Chinese mitten crabs, or find any sign of an infestation, you can help to control them by:

* If you catch a mitten crab, it's illegal to release it or allow it to escape: crushing is usually the easiest and most humane means of dispatch

* Taking careful biosecurity measures when you leave the area *(see below and page 94)*

* Reporting any sightings to the RISC or Alien Watch recording schemes *(see page 9)*

If you take part in water-based activities such as fishing, canoeing or sailing on a water body where Chinese mitten crabs are present, you can help to stop them spreading further by following the Check-Clean-Dry biosecurity guidelines *(see page 94)*.

For more information visit: **www.nonnativespecies.org**
www.environment-agency.gov.uk *and* **www.invasivespeciesireland.com**

© Cyril Bennett

FRESHWATER SHRIMP
Gammarus pulex

Where does it come from and how did it get to Ireland?

Native to England, Wales, Scotland and other parts of western Europe, *Gammarus pulex* were deliberately introduced to Northern Ireland in the 1950s by anglers trying to provide another food source for trout and salmon. They have now spread from Lough Neagh's western tributaries to Lough Erne as well as the River Boyne and rivers around Dublin.

Freshwater shrimps can grow to 2cm in length, and have been described as looking like 'swimming commas.'

Male shrimp can often be found carrying smaller females, protecting them aggressively against attackers.

What's the problem?

Ireland had no freshwater connection to Europe at the end of the last Ice Age, and a number of freshwater species, including *Gammarus pulex* and several cyprinid fish (such as chub, dace and roach) which are native to other parts of the British Isles, have become seriously invasive after being introduced to Irish rivers and loughs.

G. pulex breed quickly and predate voraciously on other species - particularly those which haven't evolved alongside them – and research shows that Ireland's native freshwater shrimp, *G. duebeni celticus*, is being driven to extinction in many areas. Both species compete by attacking and eating each others' females, but *G. pulex* males are larger and more aggressive in attacking *G. duebeni* females, and more effective in defending their own. As a result, native females disappear faster than the invaders', resulting in rapid loss of the native population. *G. pulex* are also actively migratory, and have even been observed moving upstream over weirs on the River Ballinderry by forming a continuously moving ribbon of their own bodies.

What can I do about it?

If you see *G. pulex* shrimp in Ireland, you can help to control them by:

* Taking careful biosecurity measures when you leave the area *(see below and page 94)*

* Reporting any sightings to the Alien Watch recording scheme *(see page 9)*

If you take part in water-based activities such as fishing, canoeing or sailing on a water body where *G. pulex* shrimp are present, you can help to stop them spreading further by following the Check-Clean-Dry biosecurity guidelines *(see page 94)*.

Apart from stringent biosecurity measures, no effective means of control are currently known.

© Environment Agency

PONTO-CASPIAN SHRIMP

Dikerogammarus villosus, Dikerogammarus haemobaphes

Where does it come from and how did it get here?

Several shrimp species started moving across Europe from the Black Sea region when the Rhine-Main-Danube Canal opened in 1992. *D. villosus* was found in Cardiff Bay, Grafham Water and Eglwys Nunnyd reservoir in 2010, and the Norfolk Broads by 2012. *D. haemobaphes* was confirmed in the Severn in 2012, followed by the Thames, Trent, Witham, and Kennet and Avon Canal.

D. villosus grow up to 3cm long, with cone-shaped bumps on their tails, and use their large mandibles to shred other species, leading to their popular nickname 'killer shrimp'.

D. haemobaphes may also have reached the UK in damp water sports equipment.

What's the problem?

Dikerogammarus villosus and *D. haemobaphes* are considered a very serious threat to many of the UK's native species. Both can live in rivers, canals and lakes, with low oxygen levels, a wide range of habitats and even 20% salinity.

Growing up to 3cm long, *D. villosus* are much larger than the UK's native freshwater shrimp (which ironically have also proved invasive in Ireland – *see page 80*), and are popularly known as 'killer shrimps' for their tendency to kill indiscriminately and shred many kinds of prey without eating it. Other invertebrates, fish eggs and juvenile fish are subject to voracious attack, so vulnerable species may be driven into local extinction (during its progress across Europe, *D. villosus* has even been able to displace other invasive shrimp species). Scientists think *D. haemobaphes* will have a similar impact.

What can I do about it?

If you see Ponto-Caspian shrimp, or find any sign of an infestation, you can help to control them by:

* Taking careful biosecurity measures when you leave the area *(see below and page 94)*. No other effective means of control are currently known.

* In the UK, emailing details and a photograph to:
  alert_nonnative@ceh.ac.uk

* Reporting any sightings to the RISC or Alien Watch recording schemes *(see page 9)*

If you take part in water-based activities such as fishing, canoeing or sailing on a water body where Ponto-Caspian shrimp are present, stop them spreading further by following the Check-Clean-Dry biosecurity guidelines *(see page 94)*. Environment Agency research suggests that they can tolerate very poor water quality and survive in damp areas of fishing tackle, trailers, boats and kayaks for up to 15 days.

© US Fish & Wildlife Service

QUAGGA MUSSEL

Dreissena bugensis rostriformis

Where does it come from and how do we stop it getting here?

Quagga mussels haven't yet reached the British Isles, but are steadily spreading across Europe and North America from their native range in the Dnieper River in Ukraine, often via ships' ballast water. To protect our environment and economy, any signs of invasion need to be identified as soon as possible.

Quagga mussel shells are taller and more rounded than zebra mussels, with similar zebra-like stripes.

Like zebra mussels, quagga mussels form dense colonies on hard structures, blocking pipes and lock gates, and incurring huge biofouling management costs.

What's the problem?

If they spread to Britain, quagga mussels would cause significant economic and environmental damage. Even more invasive than zebra mussels, to which they're closely related *(see pages 86-87)*, they can alter whole ecosystems by filtering vast quantities of nutrients out of rivers and lakes. This deprives juvenile fish of food and can mask the water's natural response to eutrophication, leading to sudden toxic algal blooms which may affect local peoples' drinking water. They may also cause health risks by bioaccumulating toxins and introducing them into the food chain via any fish which eat them.

Quagga mussels incur huge costs by fouling water pipes, lock gates, cooling systems, ships' hulls and other structures. The combined cost of managing invasive quagga and zebra mussels in North America's Great Lakes is thought to be at least $500 million a year.

What can I do about it?

If you see quagga mussels, or find any sign of an infestation, you can help to control them by:

* Taking careful biosecurity measures when you leave the area *(see below and page 94)*

* In the UK, emailing details and a photograph to:
  alert_nonnative@ceh.ac.uk

* In Ireland, reporting any sightings to the Alien Watch recording scheme *(see page 9)*

If you take part in water-based activities such as fishing, canoeing or sailing on a water body anywhere in Europe or North America where quagga mussels are present, you can help to stop them spreading further by following the Check-Clean-Dry biosecurity guidelines *(see page 94)*.

For more information visit:
www.nonnativespecies.org/alerts/quaggamussel
and **www.invasivespeciesireland.com**

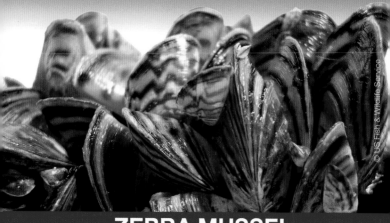

ZEBRA MUSSEL
Dreissena polymorpha

Where does it come from and how did it get here?

Having evolved in the Black Sea area, zebra mussels probably arrived in the UK on timber ships from the Baltic in the early 1820s, and dispersed rapidly through the canal network. They reached Ireland's Shannon system in the 1990s: recreational boat traffic has helped them to colonise at least another 50 loughs like Erne, Neagh and Corrib.

Above: As their name suggests, zebra mussels have distinctive stripy shells and grow up to 3-4cm long.
Zebra mussels filter nutrients out of the water, so juvenile fish may starve, and fisheries suffer.

Below: Boat propellor fouled by a colony of zebra mussels.

What's the problem?

Zebra mussels are highly efficient filter feeders which can change whole ecosystems by filtering nutrients out of suspension in lakes and rivers at a rate of at least one litre of water per mussel per day. They smother native mussels and are evolutionarily linked to several species of Ponto-Caspian shrimp: by re-depositing nutrients as excreta around their colonies, they provide an easier food source for their fellow invaders. By bio-accumulating toxins, they may also cause outbreaks of avian botulism which has killed thousands of birds on North America's Great Lakes.

Zebra mussel larvae grow into dense clusters on any available hard surface including pipes, filters, turbines and cooling systems: Anglian Water already has to spend at least £500,000 on clearing zebra mussels from its treatment plants each year, while the annual cost to water companies in North America is estimated at $5 billion.

What can I do about it?

If you see zebra mussels, or find any sign of an infestation, you can help to control them by:

✳ Taking careful biosecurity measures when you leave the area *(see below and page 94)*

✳ Reporting any sightings to the RISC or Alien Watch recording schemes *(see page 9)*

If you take part in water-based activities such as fishing, canoeing or sailing on a water body where zebra mussels are present, you can help to stop them spreading further by following the Check-Clean-Dry biosecurity guidelines *(see page 94)*.

Juvenile mussels may appear as a rough texture on boat hulls: if infestation is heavy or you don't have enough time to air dry for 4-5 weeks, high pressure steam cleaning above 400°C is recommended.

For more information visit: **www.nonnativespecies.org**
www.environment.agency.gov.uk and www.invasivespeciesireland.com

INVASIVE PARASITES & PATHOGENS

Like Dutch elm disease which devastated the UK's elm trees after it arrived in 1957, there's a whole host of nearly-invisible invasive pathogens and parasites which also threaten our native species and landscapes. These include:

Ash dieback (*Chalara fraxinea*) hit the headlines in 2012 when it was detected on saplings from the Netherlands in a nursery in Buckinghamshire. This fungus is now found across the UK, causing leaf loss and dieback before killing affected trees completely.

Chytrid fungus (*Batrachochytrium dendrobatidis*) is a parasite causing mass global extinctions of frogs, newts and other amphibians. It is carried by resistant species like the American bullfrog, and has been called 'the worst infectious disease ever recorded among vertebrates in terms of the number of species impacted, and its propensity to drive them to extinction'.

Crayfish plague (*Aphanomyces astaci*) is a water mould carried by American signal crayfish. Invariably deadly to the UK's native white-clawed crayfish, its spores can survive for up to 2 weeks on damp water sports equipment or crayfish traps.

Salmon fluke (*Gyrodactylus salaris*) is a tiny leech-like parasite which also affects trout, grayling and other salmonid fish. Although it hasn't yet reached the UK, its impact in Scandinavia has virtually wiped out salmon in more than 40 Norwegian rivers since 1970. It has also been found in Germany, France, Portugal and Spain.

Sudden oak death is caused by *Phytophthora ramorum*, a fungus-like pathogen which produces bleeding cankers on infected trees' trunks, and kills larch and chestnut trees as well as oaks. First reported in a garden centre in Sussex in 2002, it can be spread by mists, air currents, footwear, car and bicycle tyres, and animals' paws.

Varroatosis is a serious threat to bees caused by parasitic *Varroa destructor* mites which reached the UK in 1992. The mites transmit a range of diseases including deformed wing virus: untreated bee colonies die within 2-3 years.

HELP STOP THESE PATHOGENS AND PARASITES SPREADING:

Find the latest biosecurity guidelines at
www.nonnativespecies.org/biosecurity

VOLUNTEERING: HOW CAN I HELP?

At the UK's first third-sector biosecurity conference in 2011, government scientists estimated it would cost at least £300m to eradicate Himalayan balsam from the UK. "We can't afford to take that high risk strategy," they admitted, "but if you want to prevent it affecting your interests at a local level, go for it!"

Today, government agencies still fund efforts to clear INNS like floating pennywort when they increase the risk of flooding, and intervene directly to try to eradicate some high risk species such as topmouth gudgeon and American bullfrogs before they become established. But when it comes to tackling more widespread plants and animals, there are many well co-ordinated partnership projects where local volunteers and members of the public are playing a very important role – with target INNS ranging from Himalayan balsam to rhododendron, skunk cabbage and mink.

In Herefordshire and Monmouthshire, for instance, thousands of freely-donated volunteer hours have already helped clear invasive mink and Himalayan balsam from the River Monnow and its tributaries as part of the Monnow Rivers Association's trailblazing Going Native project since 2010.

To remove Himalayan balsam, teams of volunteers followed up on initial spraying by contractors, pulling late-germinating plants to stop them setting seed *(see page 12)*. Local EA staff spent their annual environmental leave working on the project, and visiting anglers were asked to pull 50 plants each during their day out on the river. By 2014, the whole 75km Monnow system should be almost clear of Himalayan balsam – the very first river catchment in the UK to achieve this result.

Meanwhile, the MRA's volunteers (and one part-time paid co-ordinator) have also been working on the Monnow's long-standing mink problem, running a network of more than 100 mink rafts to detect and trap these voracious predators *(see page 42)*. With 60 traps still in place to intercept 7 or 8 invaders every year, the Monnow is now the only UK river where mink have been successfully eradicated, making it possible to reintroduce nationally-threatened water voles without fear they'll be swiftly killed.

Find out more at **www.monnow.org**

Other successful volunteer projects across the UK and Ireland include:

Ballinderry River Enhancement Association: eradicating giant hogweed and other INNS

Bollin NNS Local Action Group: mobilising volunteers to raise awareness and co-ordinate tackling Himalayan balsam, giant hogweed and Japanese knotweed

Calder & Colne Rivers Trust: floating pennywort clearance by spraying and hand pulling

Dorset Wildlife Trust: rhododendron control and woodland regeneration for red squirrels on Brownsea Island

Hampshire Wildlife Trust: working with local voluntary champions to control INNS throughout Hampshire and the Isle of Wight

South Cumbria Rivers Trust: freshwater biosecurity planning and co-ordination

Inland Fisheries Ireland: CAISIE EU LIFE+ project managing aquatic INNS on Lough Corrib, the Grand Canal and Barrow Navigation

Norfolk Non-Native Species Initiative: citizen science surveys and action weekends to tackle water primrose, Australian swamp stonecrop, parrot's feather and floating pennywort

South Cumbria Rivers Trust: freshwater biosecurity planning and co-ordination

Thames 21 and the Wandle Trust: Himalayan balsam and floating pennywort pulling across south London

Tweed Invasives Forum: tackling giant hogweed and Japanese knotweed with local river champions including anglers, farmers and other landowners

It's easy to get involved! Search online for your local projects today!

HEALTH & SAFETY

When you're tackling INNS of any kind, it's vital to take steps to make sure you and other people stay safe.

Use this list of suggestions as your starting point, and remember there's no substitute for common sense!

✳ Carry out a careful risk assessment before starting any work, and consider getting insurance for complicated tasks and larger groups of people (for more information, visit: www.tcv.org.uk)

✳ Wear appropriate protective clothing, including gloves, long sleeves, trousers and suitably sturdy footwear. Watch the weather and be aware of the risks of heat (sunburn, dehydration or heat stroke) or cold and wet (hypothermia)

✳ If you're working around water, consider wearing a lifejacket, plus other protective clothing such as steel–shanked and toecapped waders. Beware of steep or undercut banks, and use a long stick to test the depth in muddy areas: if you feel yourself sinking, don't panic, but move calmly back out again the same way you went in

✳ Working in areas where rats are present, including ponds and river banks, may involve the risk of Weil's disease (*leptospirosis*), a bacterial infection carried in rats' urine which can be fatal if not treated correctly. Carry a first aid kit, cover any cuts or grazes with waterproof plasters, always wash your hands before eating, drinking or smoking, and consult your doctor if you develop flu-like symptoms within 2-3 weeks of working in these environments

✳ If your INNS management involves an air rifle or firearm, it's your responsibility to get all appropriate permissions and know the laws relating to shooting and target species in your area. Never point the muzzle of your rifle in an unsafe direction; take account of where your bullet may end up if you miss your target, and avoid ricochets. It's illegal to shoot within 50ft of a road if anyone on it is injured, interrupted or endangered. Visit: www.basc.org.uk

STOP THE SPREAD

Wherever you are, you can help stop unwelcome INNS spreading into new areas by following these guidelines from the **GB Non-Native Species Secretariat** and **Invasive Species Ireland**:

 CHECK: All clothing and equipment should be thoroughly inspected and any visible debris (mud, plant or animal matter) should be removed and left at the water body where it was found. Particular attention must be paid to the seams and seals of boots and waders. Any pockets of pooled water should be emptied.

 CLEAN: Equipment should be hosed down or pressure-washed on site. If facilities are not available equipment should be carefully contained, eg in plastic bags, until they can be found. Washings should be left at the water body where the equipment was used, or contained and not allowed to enter any other watercourse or drainage system (ie do not put them down the drain or sink). Where possible, clean equipment should be dipped in disinfectant solution (eg. Virkon) to kill diseases, but note this is unlikely to kill non-native species.

 DRY: Thoroughly drying is the best method for disinfecting clothing and equipment. Boots and nets should be hung up to dry. Equipment should be thoroughly dry for 48 hours before it is used elsewhere. Some non-native species can survive for as many as 15 days in damp conditions and up to 2 days in dry conditions.

BE PLANT WISE: Stop the spread by not moving pond plants around. Even tiny plant fragments can lead to massive problems, so be careful when maintaining your pond or aquarium and disposing of waste water. Any waste water should be emptied away from streams, rivers, ponds, lakes and lochs, or drains that flow into them. You could use the excess water on the lawn or to water plants in your garden.

 BE PET WISE: Most pet owners are responsible and well-informed, but many pets can harm our native species if they escape or are released into the wild. Pets which grow very large, breed easily, or need special care, are considered most likely to become invasive. From goldfish, cats and rabbits to more unusual birds, fish and amphibians, escaped pets can have a disastrous impact on natural biodiversity. Be responsible with pets, keep them in such a way that they can't escape, and don't let them become invasive.

For more information visit:

www.nonnativespecies.org/checkcleandry
www.nonnativespecies.org/beplantwise
www.invasivespeciesireland.com/what-can-i-do/pets

ACKNOWLEDGEMENTS

Many people have been hugely helpful with the preparation of this pocket guide. In particular, I'd like to thank:

✳ My publishers **Merlin**, **Karen** and **Jo** for spotting the idea for this book embedded in my earlier book *Trout in Dirty Places* (Merlin Unwin Books 2012) and working enthusiastically to help me develop it.

✳ **Niall Moore** (GBNNSS), **Bella Davies** (Wandle Trust), **Jo Heisse** (EA), **Karen Harper** (LISI), **Dave Webb** (EA) and **Trevor Renals** (EA) for providing professional comments and helpful suggestions, and reading drafts at various stages of completeness.

✳ **Lucy Cornwell** (GBNNSS) for her help in supplying many key photos. **Joe Caffrey** (Central Fisheries Board) for his help with photos and a perspective on Ireland's INNS. **Ian Bedford** and **Les Noble** for advice on Spanish slugs.

✳ **Rob Francis** for lending me his superbly authoritative *Handbook of Global Invasive Freshwater Species*.

✳ **Rob Collins** for supplying an insightful Rivers Trust perspective.

✳ **Rob Denny, Patrick Lloyd, Neil Marfell** and **Peter Lapsley** for information and photos from the Monnow project. The photos on pages 6-7 first appeared in Peter's thoroughly researched article 'Monitoring the Monnow' in the February 2012 issue of *Fly Fishing & Fly Tying* magazine. **Alexandra Mileham** for her very helpful gardener's point of view.

✳ To all those, listed individually on the appropriate pages, who have generously allowed me to reproduce their photos in this book.

✳ And most of all to my wife **Sally** and our cocker spaniel **Winnie** for their tireless support and encouragement. No Himalayan balsam or grey squirrels are safe while they're around!